see saw

see saw

An anthology of poetry and artwork around science by children from Rockland St Mary County Primary School and Framingham Earl High School, working with Matthew Sweeney and Jill Pirrie

Edited by Anne Osbourn, Jill Pirrie, John Nicholson, Ken Holbeck and Sally Hogden

the saw press

Published by the SAW Press
18 Lower Road
Rockland St Mary
Norwich
NR14 7HS
info@sawtrust.org

ISBN 0-9550180-0-5

Designed by Wiz Graphics
Printed in Great Britain by Norwich Colour Print

Front cover: Ammonite by Emily Nicol Y5
Rockland St Mary County Primary School

Science, Art and Writing

a new way of looking at the world

contents

Acknowledgements

SAW was initiated and developed by Anne Osbourn during her National Endowment for Science, Technology and the Arts (NESTA)-funded Dream Time Fellowship. The support of the Sainsbury Laboratory and the School of Literature and Creative Writing at the University of East Anglia is also gratefully acknowledged.

We would especially like to thank Professor Louise Swiniarski, Dr Allan Shwedel and colleagues (School of Education, Salem State College, Mass., USA) for their advice, support and comments during the development of this project. We would like to thank Sandy Lowe, Siân Davies, Denise McGee, Sarah Carter, Sue Burrell, Sally Rix, Wendy Charalambous (Rockland St Mary County Primary School) and John Patchett, Hazel Garrity and Wendy Down (Framingham Earl High School) for the time, energy and enthusiasm that they have put into this project. We would also like to pay tribute to all of the children who took part; not only were they inspired, they have been inspirational.

Special thanks go to Matthew Sweeney for his creativity and input. We thank Naomi Jaffa (Director of The Poetry Trust) and Jane Anderson (The Poetry Trust's Education and Outreach worker) for their encouragement and involvement, and for arranging for Matthew to visit Rockland St Mary County Primary School. We also thank Ann Oliver and Jeni Smith (School of Education and Lifelong Learning, University of East Anglia) and Sarah Passingham for their helpful comments, and the Science Photo Library for supplying images.

Finally, many thanks to George Szirtes for permission to use the quote on page 9.

Anne Osbourn, Jill Pirrie, John Nicholson, Ken Holbeck and Sally Hogden

introduction

Creativity and excellence in science, art and writing depend on real insight – on the ability to focus, to observe, to note detail, to extract the essence, to pinpoint the truth *as you see it*, and then to express this truth clearly and succinctly to others. This kind of insight can only come into being when the truth-seeker has a genuine empathy with his or her subject that stems from a hunger, from an insatiable need to explore and understand.

Visual images are a wonderful starting point for adventures of this kind. Striking photographs of science have entrancing qualities; they are crying out to be explored through words, spoken or written, and through art. This union of science, art and creative writing around a central scientific focus (a concept that I have initiated and named 'SAW') represents a powerful way of bringing science into our everyday lives and language. It also promotes new ways of stimulating creativity, exploration and learning that inspire and excite individuals of all ages and abilities.

We all look at things in different ways. Together we can draw on our strengths and differences to build up a patchwork of understanding, a better approximation of the truth. Through this we may hope to develop a deeper knowledge and enjoyment of the world that we live in, and to learn how best to protect, sustain and nurture it. This book is a collection of truths from children ranging in age from four to twelve, grouped into three themes – 'The Earth and Beyond', 'Under the Microscope' and 'Senses'. Each child took their own personal journey, starting from a scientific image of their choice, through thoughts, exploration and feelings, to arrive at the finishing points that you find in these pages. During their journeys they were supported by teachers, scientists, poets and artists. It became apparent that in many cases this was not the finishing point, but the beginning of a whole new way of looking at the world.

Anne Osbourn

'Poetry's only obligation is to the truth. Whether this truth is widely popular or not is irrelevant. It should be the best truth possible and that is the only quality that gives it any hope of survival.' George Szirtes (*The Guardian*, April 9th 2005).

The same is true of art and science.

the earth and beyond

The Earth from space
Satellite image of the Earth showing the continent of
Europe at the centre and north Africa at the bottom.
The satellite is a man-made device that has been
launched into orbit around the earth. It is being used
for remote sensing of the Earth and its environment.

Image: PLI/Science Photo Library

space

Earth-sick Astronaut

I long to see a face other than my own in the
Sleek surfaces of space.

I long to hear a sound other than the
Occasional crackle of the static on the radio.

I long to smell sizzling bacon on a hot stove, not the
Cold metallic odour of loneliness.

I long to feel clear, white water trickling
Through the tiny gaps between my fingers.

I long to be in my warm home,
To wake up from my dreams in a place
Where I'm not roped down by the blackness

Of Space.

Jack Sutton Y7
Framingham Earl High School

Looking Back

Out here I can see
Your world going round and round.
Rocks crashing
Down and down.
Pigs snorting
Louder and louder.
People on the Great Wall of China,
Dancing the cha cha cha.

Group poem Reception, Y1 and Y2
Rockland St Mary County Primary School

Earth Sick

As I touch the cold buttons
I remember holding my baby brother Dylan
When I touched his head so soft.
As I hear strange noises
I miss my brother Finley
Chatting away even as I don't understand
What he's saying.
As I sit in my hard chair
I remember my mum cuddling me.

Ayla Evans Y4
Rockland St Mary County Primary School

Space

As my space ship hurtles into outer space
Into the dark abyss,
No smell, no sound, no taste,
I remember Earth.

Group poem Y3 and Y4
Rockland St Mary County Primary School

Jasmine Smith Y1
Rockland St Mary County Primary School

Lost in Space

I'm lost in space.
I want to hear the sound of the ball when it crashes into
The back of the net.

I want to see a bonfire flickering away in the darkness.

I want to smell chips when they are in a paper bag when
The smell creeps out through the gaps.

I want to touch fresh baked bread and feel the squidgy
Hole that my finger can make.

I'm lost,
Lost,
Lost
In
Space.

Sam Larnder Y7
Framingham Earl High School

Missing

I miss the sweet smell
Of the fresh garden.
I miss the touch of
Bark on the trees.
Here in outer space
There are few things to see.
I miss the taste of
Popcorn at the cinema.
The soft touch of my hamster.
The springing enjoyment of Spring.

Millie Crouch Y4
Rockland St Mary County Primary School

Memories from Earth

I miss the first sweet taste of strawberries.
The soft fur when I lay
My hand across my cat.
The strong thick smell of honey.
Oh how I do miss the crunch of snow
That melts into cold water
And swimming the butterfly
And the dolphin.

Reuben Braden-Bell Y4
Rockland St Mary County Primary School

Earth Memories

I miss my ponies in their winter fluff
As they click their hooves
In the air on the wall,
The fluff of their fur
Curled against me.

Ruth Gayton Y3
Rockland St Mary County Primary School

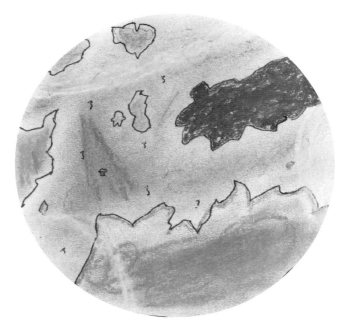

Yasmin High Y6
Rockland St Mary County Primary School

The Yellow Moon of Jupiter

Whizzing past the many stars
Whooshing past Jupiter and Mars,
Almost there, the time is noon.
I am trying to visit the Yellow Moon!
Quite often the Yellow Moon turns inside out,
Volcanoes arriving all about.
Imagine a strawberry flavour jelly-like floor,
Wibbling and wobbling,
Show me the door!
Lava and molten rock spilling everywhere,
Houses fall down all the time, BEWARE!
Bright dotty creatures jumping, eating
Others giving each other a good hard beating!
Suddenly the whole moon starts to shake,
It looks like it's about to break.
I jump into my space ship quick,
Just as all the volcanoes start to spit.
I start to lift off, just in time
Quickly every dotty creature starts to climb
Up the trees that are the colour of lime!
I look out of my small circular window
It looks like it's about to blow!
A large crack appears down the side
As each little creature starts to slide.

Sophie Allinson Y5
Rockland St Mary County Primary School

Matthew Lodge Y5
Rockland St Mary County Primary School

The Yellow Moon

The yellow moon is full of craters,
Volcanoes to be precise.
Like a spherical, fit to burst balloon.
The astronauts will be there soon
To investigate the bulbous holes
That look like they've been made
By giant moles.

Peter Cullum Y5
Rockland St Mary County Primary School

Yellow Moon Haiku

The yellow moon wakes
The sun, the sun is angry,
He shouts really loud.

Callum Regan and Frankie Evans Y5
Rockland St Mary County Primary School

Yellow Moon

Yellow planet glowing in the dark
Always exploding, new volcanoes
Inside turning outside turning in,
Gliding through on my space ship,
Warmed by the lava spurting out,
On to molten rock.
One of Jupiter's many moons.
New volcanoes shoot from the ground.

Abigail Pritchard Y6
Rockland St Mary County Primary School

ammonites

The Spiral Staircase

A spiral never ending staircase
Dropping down, down to where it begins
In the sea
One day you will be washed on the beach
Fossilised on the rocks.

Daniel Crabb Y4
Rockland St Mary County Primary School

Shannon Parfitt Y3
Rockland St Mary County Primary School

My Ammonite

Spiralling patterns
Brightly coloured detail
Never ending stairs
Thousands of steps
Pink, blue, green
Not forgetting purple
All filled in
Colours of the sea
Watch the ammonite
Squirt across the seabed
No matter what size
Big or small
Keep swimming ammonite
Always reach your destination.

Evie Pettit Y5
Rockland St Mary County Primary School

Chloe Williams Y4
Rockland St Mary County Primary School

The Spinning Ammonite

The ammonite spins,
Spins like sparks of rainbow colours
When it rains and the sun is out.
Red, blue and pink,
Swirling a gold of light,
A catherine wheel.

Shannon Parfitt Y3
Rockland St Mary County Primary School

Alex White Y3
Rockland St Mary County Primary School

Spiral

A spiral staircase
Sinking down and down
Into the start of time.

As a sea creature it swam.
Over time it turned to stone,
A colosseum packed with seats
It dies.

Ready for its big drop
To the sea floor.
One day it will crop up
Stuck to a rock.

Reuben Braden-Bell Y4
Rockland St Mary County Primary School

Jake Brown Y3
Rockland St Mary County
Primary School

Evie Pettit Y5
Rockland St Mary County
Primary School

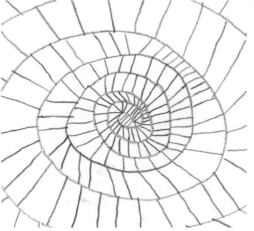

William Gayton Y6
Rockland St Mary County
Primary School

Ben Swarbrick Y6
Rockland St Mary County Primary School

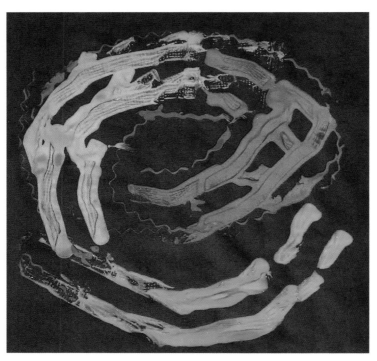

Emily Leeson Reception
Rockland St Mary County Primary School

lightning

Night of Frights

The crack throughout the sky
Broke the edge of the earth,
Striking silver on a purple background,
Flickering flashes all night,
Streaming lava, a bolt of electricity
Whizzing through the air,
See the glittering light, hear the ear-breaking sounds.
Power volts hurtle for hours on end
Throwing lightning at the earth.

Bella Tait and Yasmin High Y6
Rockland St Mary County Primary School

Oliver Wakefield Reception
Rockland St Mary County Primary School

Striking

The sky is black, no sound, no sound,
Then suddenly the canvas sky is painted
With streaks of silver and purple,
Some straight, some square, some round.
It's like bolts of electricity trying to get to the floor.
The deafening crack in the shape of a not quite right sword
As long as a whip and thick as a tree.
But then as if it was never there, it's gone.
The sky is black, no sound, no sound.
Apart from the quivering tree
Waiting for the next attack.

Ollie Johnson-Roberts Y6
Rockland St Mary County Primary School

Erin Luck and Isobel Hunt Y7
Framingham Earl High School

under the microscope

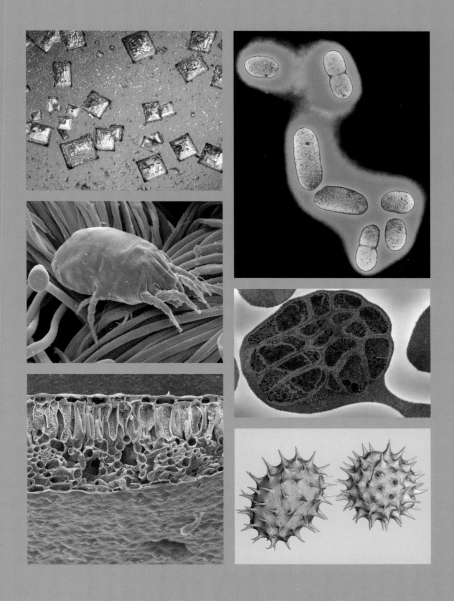

salt crystals

Salt Under the Microscope

A mountain in a bowl of white
Then,
Shining silver digs
Into the mound.
A flash of rainbow
Sparkles in squares of light,
No longer crystals
But salt.

Kathryn Evans Y4
Rockland St Mary County Primary School

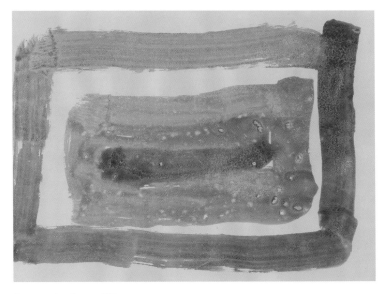

James Jackson Y1
Rockland St Mary County Primary School

Amelia Rix Y4
Rockland St Mary County Primary School

Salt Crystals

Squares falling from the sky,
Square pictures floating in the sky,
Kites flying up into the sky,
A sunset with ice cubes,
Little pictures falling,
Diamonds sparkling,
Kaleidoscope.

Collective thoughts Reception, Y1 and Y2
Rockland St Mary County Primary School

Salt Crystals

I see you salt crystals
Fizz to the top of the lemonade.
If I squash you too hard
You crunch into hundreds of pieces.
If you fall off the table and
Onto the floor
You will scatter for evermore.
If you pop into water you disappear
Like magic.

Amelia Land and Hannah Burrell Y3
Rockland St Mary County Primary School

escherichia coli

Inside my Tummy

I've some of the weirdest
Things inside my body!
A pet of mine which
Is very strange and small;
It's called *Escherichia coli*
And lives by feeding on
Things in my tummy.
It splits into two to
Create more *E. colis*.
They're so small that
You would need a
Microscope to see them.

Ryan Pettit Y6
Rockland St Mary County Primary School

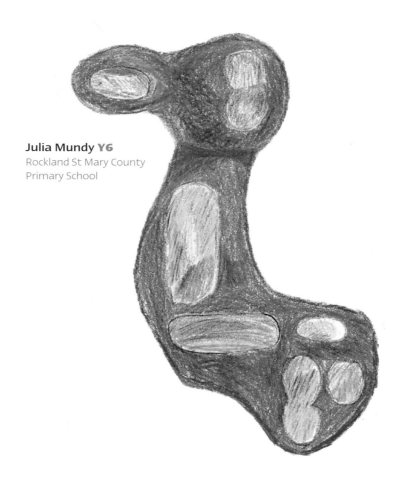

Julia Mundy Y6
Rockland St Mary County
Primary School

The Green Duck

The *E. coli* look like tablets
Inside a green duck,
But they are tiny bacteria
Living in me.
First they are friendly
But turn evil,
Turn quite bad
To make me sick.

Chloe Davidson Y3
Rockland St Mary County Primary School

dust mites

Dirty Dust Mite

Dirty dust mite.
You are so microscopic
I need an instrument to see you.
Thousands of your friends live in my bed.
Your name is *Dermatophagoides*,
A hard name to pronounce,
So I call you derma for short.
You live on my cuff near the edge.
My cat hates you because you make her sneeze.
You bounce around on my carpet
But I know just where you are because
I can see you with my sensitive eyes.
You look like a small hoover bag,
You're always annoying my brother's hamster
And making him itch.
But I won't replace you,
You are my dust mite, derma.

Julia Mundy Y6
Rockland St Mary County Primary School

My Pet

My pet is a special pet
Because it eats 70% of skin.
You will need a microscope
To help people to find him.

Matthew Lodge Y5
Rockland St Mary County Primary School

Under the Microscope Hunter

Crawling through a
Forest of hair.
Finding its dust.
Spreading infection.
Legs infecting
The carpet fibre hairs.
A monster
Climbing tangled reeds.

Patrick Ellison Y3
Rockland St Mary County Primary School

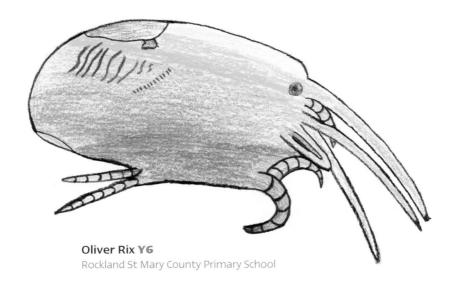

Oliver Rix Y6
Rockland St Mary County Primary School

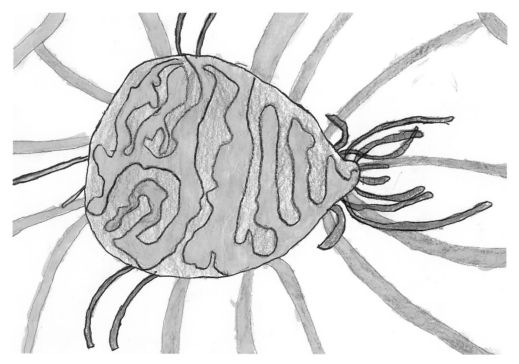

Andrew Crabb Y6
Rockland St Mary County Primary School

Dust Mite Scurry

Scurry, scurry, dust mite scurry,
Along the carpeted floor,
Scratching the fibres,
A hurricane of power,
Blasting the dust mite away,
Into the vacuum of space.
The dust mite won't be seen
Again.

Toby Dunlop Y7
Framingham Earl High School

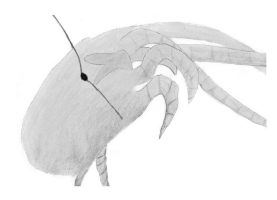

Sophie Allinson Y5
Rockland St Mary County
Primary School

Fabric

I call my dust mite Fabric,
I have speakers
That translate his voice
And make it louder.
He feeds on dead skin and dust,
He is potato shaped
And makes me sneeze.
No wonder,
He lives in my collar!

Andrew Crabb and Ollie Johnson-Roberts Y6
Rockland St Mary County Primary School

malaria

Malaria

An invading force is coming, coming.
I can hear cries of evil and fear.
If you touch it feels jagged and hard.
It wants to kill you...and it will.

I see the bug moving from cell to cell
But every time leaving damage and hell.
You can't stop it.
You cannot get it out.
It's invading and it's here to stay.

I hear screaming and shouting and
Pounding of feet but now it's silent
Because life's been covered by
A black sheet, nothing more.

Joe Robson Y7
Framingham Earl High School

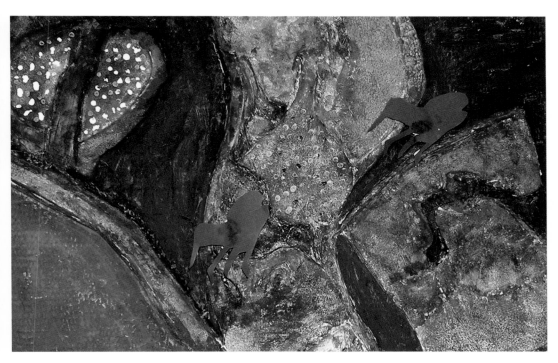

Phoebe Wall Palmer and Mercede Faber Y7
Framingham Earl High School

christmas rose leaves

Under the Microscope

Here is a lively ocean, splashing,
playing. Swirling and rippling round
and round. An island in the distance,
lonely and unharmed. A salty smell
and fresh air taste. A luminous
turquoise gaining in depth. Occasional
shades of red and white reflected
in the sun, lost in the sea. Greens
of seaweed tangled, churning,
searching for a way out. Its
purpose is to breathe in and out,
in and out, a relaxed movement.
Each ripple, each wave has a
shore and will do anything to
reach it.

Rebecca Spanner Y7
Framingham Earl High School

A Christmas Rose Leaf

The inside of a leaf looks like the sea
With plants growing and a cave collapsing.
The whale calls for a friend to swim with him.
The waves crash and splash against each other.

Jacob Beckley Y4
Rockland St Mary County Primary School

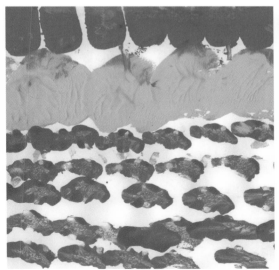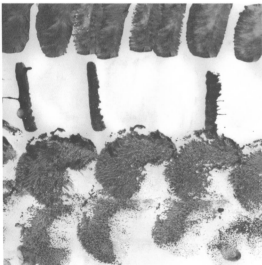

Ryan Smith Y1
Rockland St Mary County Primary School

Thoughts on a Christmas Rose Leaf

Bumpy,
A tadpole,
Looks like a mountain,
Rough, oval shape,
A coral reef,
A whale swimming in an underground cave,
A picture taken under the sea by a diver,
A cliff with a lighthouse on top.

Collective thoughts Reception, Y1 and Y2
Rockland St Mary County Primary School

Struggle for Life

Here I see cliffs of sea green,
Craters of brown and blue,
The cells are swimming,
Drowning,
Then many are found.

I feel waves,
Lapping against rocks,
Arches of candle wax,
Running through the labyrinth
Of dark holes and unknown curves.

I smell the salty sea,
And the honeycomb pieces,
I hear voices of motivation,
And the struggle for life.

Phoebe Wall Palmer Y7
Framingham Earl High School

pollen grains

Andrew Parfitt and Joe Robson Y7
Framingham Earl High School

Daniel Gentle Y3
Rockland St Mary County
Primary School

Sunflower Pollen Grain

I see a sunflower pollen grain
With a honey yellow middle.
Then I look through a microscope,
I see a puffer fish,
Very silly.
A spikey wonder.
But why do I see a sunflower pollen grain?

Daniel Gentle Y3
Rockland St Mary County Primary School

senses

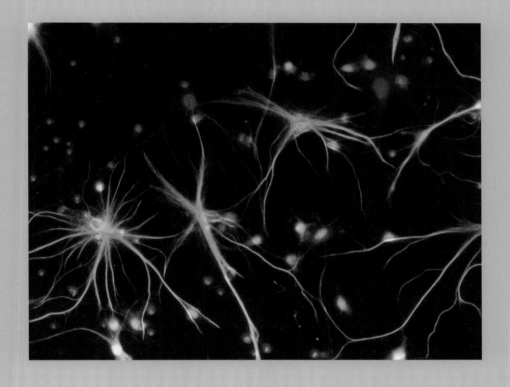

Nerve cells
The image shows nerve cells (pink) and star-shaped astrocyte cells (green) inside the spine. Astrocyte cells provide support and nutrients for the nerve cells and it is thought that they may store information. The blue dots are the nuclei (the control centres) of other support cells. Magnification: approximately x600.

Image: Nancy Kedersha/UCLA/Science Photo Library

nerve cells

Nerves

Bursting with colour,
Like fireworks filling the sky.
Nerves sending messages to the brain,
Sparks flying around the body,
Bright colours floating through
Arms and legs.
Flashes magnified thousands of times,
Planted seeds sown in the night.

Millie Crouch Y4
Rockland St Mary County Primary School

Nerve Cells

Glittering fireworks launched
In the midnight sky,
Electric forces exploding
In the black night
Creating stars in their path.

Matthew Stokes Y4 and Max Allinson Y3
Rockland St Mary County Primary School

Nerve Cells

Twisting, tangling, tossing
Turning
In their black abyss.

Trees of power
They could change your life
Spinning up your spine.

Dancing, laughing
Twisting, spinning
Gossiping with your brain.

Alex Marshall Y7
Framingham Earl High School

Hot, Hot Tea

Hot, hot tea
Erupting out of the spout
Into the cup,
Blistering heat
Pouring out,
Leaving stains
On the table.
I can see this
With my heat
Vision goggles.
The tea's all gone.
Time for another cup.

Peter Cullum and Jacob Buckland Y5
Rockland St Mary County Primary School

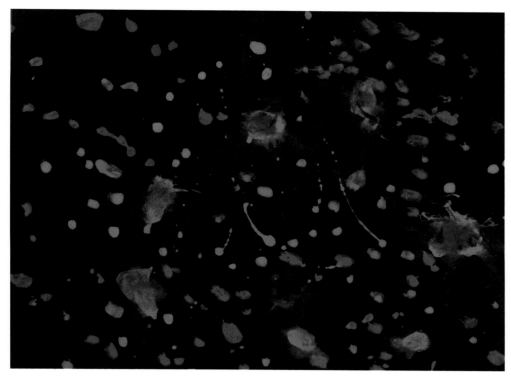

Max Allinson Y3
Rockland St Mary County Primary School

Nerve Cells

Dashes of brightly coloured street lamps,
Lighting the way!

Katy Leeson Y4
Rockland St Mary County Primary School

reflections

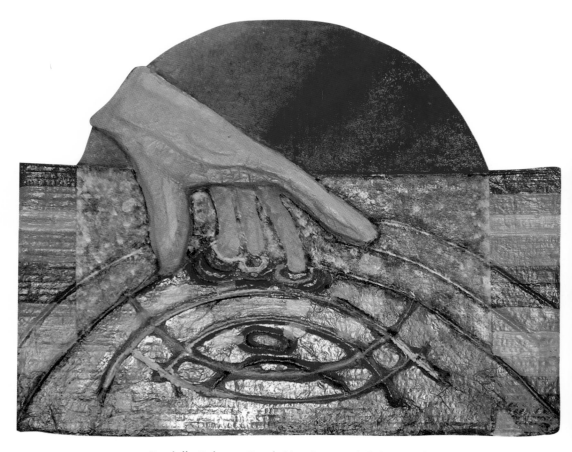

Danielle Palmer, Sarah Marrison and Claire Sugden Y7
Framingham Earl High School

Jacob Beckley Y4
Rockland St Mary County Primary School

Fish Tank

Staring at the water, my face ripples along.
The fish dances about, up my nose and back.
Clumps of rock form in my hair, weed tattoos my cheeks.
A stream of bubbles streak my face.
Ruined as the water carries it away.

Amelia Rix Y4
Rockland St Mary County Primary School

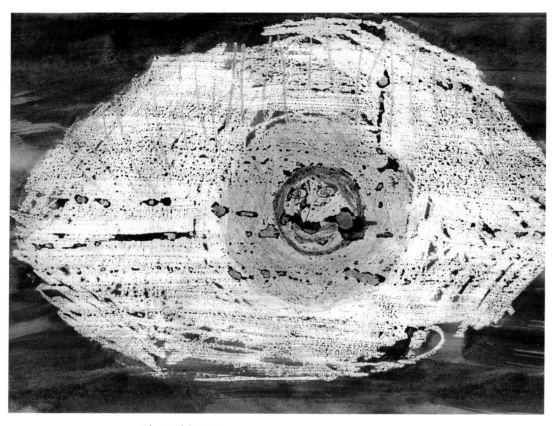

Alex White Y3
Rockland St Mary County Primary School

Classroom Computer

The mouse scampers in one ear
Out of the other.
The internet is running.
WAIT!
Birds fly in and out of the website.

Katy Leeson Y4
Rockland St Mary County Primary School

The Bread Maker Reflects

I see myself in the bread maker.
I move my head side to side slowly,
My face sprints quickly across.
Out pops the bread,
Smudges my face in the metal.

Daniel Crabb Y4
Rockland St Mary County Primary School

Colour Everywhere

This is the smudge of the world.
White piece of paper splattered with ink.
Mud moulded into a picture.
Colour collage painted with care.
It's a world of beautiful folds.
A swirl of orange, blues, greens, pinks and reds.
Brain nerves spark into life.
Yellow moon, where up there?
100000000000000000000000000000000000 miles
An hour in my spaceship.
Hot burning lava flowing out
Like salt into a sea.
You can also see the world
Your world, my world
Water dripping on water, a splash of a smile.
A pair of rather interesting, glowing cats.
A microscopic dust mite.
This is the smudge of our world.

Bella Tait Y6
Rockland St Mary County Primary School

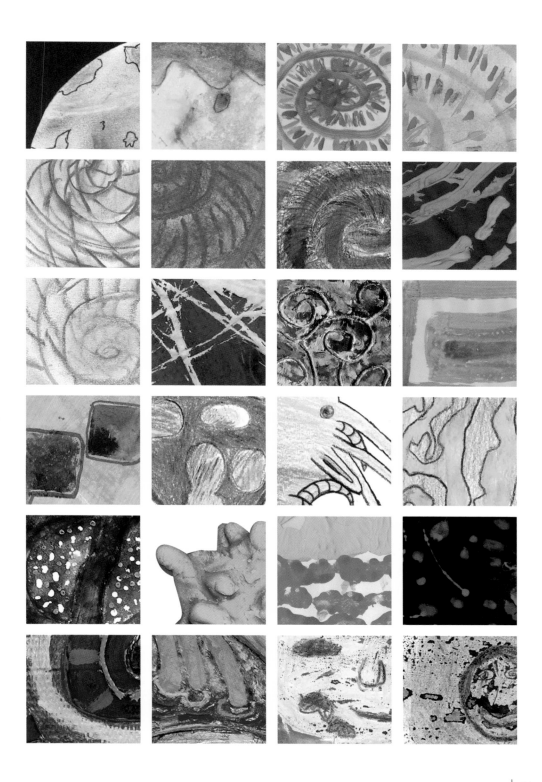

index of contributors

Rockland St Mary County Primary School

Framingham Earl High School

saw™
science art writing